COLORS

Brighten the School

Written by Stephen Moffitt
Illustrated by Peggy Tagel

Allan Publishers, Inc.

The bus is here to take Sam and Jenny to school. "I like our new bags," says Jenny. "<u>Orange</u> is my favorite color."

"There are pretty colors all around us. Let's see what other colors we can find at school," says Sam.

Sam and Jenny see their friends
on the bus. The children open
their lunch bags to see
what is inside.

**Sam looks out the window.
"The sky is <u>blue</u>," he says.
"It is the same color as the sea."**

Sam and Jenny are happy to get to school. But Jenny sees a girl crying.

"Don't be scared," says Jenny. "We will have fun. Let's go into the bright <u>red</u> schoolhouse."

There is a big board on the wall in the classroom. The teacher writes on it.

"Jenny, do you know what color
that board is?" asks Sam.
"It is <u>black</u>," answers Jenny.

After lunch, the children play outside. Jenny and her new friend fly a kite.

"The kite is <u>green</u>," says Jenny. "It is the same color as the grass."

Sam hears a buzzing sound.
He follows the sound to a flower.
A bee is sitting on the flower.

"Teacher, look," says Sam.
"The bee is <u>yellow</u>,
just like the sun."

The children sing in music class.
Then the children paint in art class.

Jenny paints a picture of a sailboat. "My sailboat is <u>white</u>. It is the same color as the clouds outside," she says.

It is time to go home. "School was fun today," says Jenny.

"And we have found so many colors," says Sam. "Orange, blue, red, black, green, yellow, and white."